PIG JIGS

Written by Nora Gaydos ■ Illustrated by BB Sams

innovative KIDS®

A pig.

A pig and a wig.

A big pig jigs.

A big pig jigs on a hill.

A big pig jigs on a hill and slips.

A big pig jigs on a hill and slips on a wig.

SLIPS and FLIPS!

A big pig hits his hips.

No jigs!

A big pig sits still on the hill.

After You Read

Answer these questions about the story, and then use words from the story in fun, new ways!

1. What does the pig slip on?
   Why does the pig sit still at the end?

2. What words rhyme with *pig*?
   What words rhyme with *hill*?
   What words rhyme with *sit*?

3. Make up a sentence of your very own for each of these words: *wig, slip, still.*
   Now try to use all of those words together in *one* sentence!